HÄGAR
THE HORRIBLE

© 1996 King Features Syndicate Inc
Published by

Pedigree ®
BOOKS

Pedigree Books Limited
The Old Rectory
Matford Lane, Exeter
Devon EX2 4PS
ISBN 1.874507.78.3
Printed in Italy

£4.99

HA2

HAMLET   LUCKY EDDIE   HÄGAR   HELGA   SNERT   HONI

SON, YOU SHOULD ALWAYS WALK TALL AND HOLD YOUR HEAD UP HIGH!

UNLESS, OF COURSE, YOU HAPPEN TO BE WALKING THROUGH A COW PASTURE

DO YOU MAKE MAPLE SYRUP FROM YOUR MAPLE TREES?

YES

WHERE DO YOU KEEP THE SAP?

RIGHT NOW HE'S INSIDE TAKING A NAP

CHRIS BROWNE

WHERE'S MOM?

SHE WENT TO HER GOURMET COOKING CLASS

TODAY WE'LL LEARN HOW TO PERK UP A MEATLOAF WITH JUST A FEW SIMPLE INGREDIENTS!

CHRIS BROWNE
3-16

THERE'S ONE GOOD THING ABOUT PLAYING POKER WITH VIKINGS...

NO ONE EVER CHEATS!

©1995 by King Features Syndicate, Inc. World rights reserved.

WHEN YOUR FATHER IS AWAY I LIKE TO LET SNERT EAT IN HERE WITH US

IT MAKES ME FEEL LIKE YOUR FATHER IS RIGHT HERE IN THE SAME ROOM...

CHOMP! CHOMP! SLURP! SLURP! GULP! SLOP!

©1995 by King Features Syndicate, Inc. World rights reserved.

YOU MISS SO MUCH ON THESE SHORT BUSINESS TRIPS TO FOREIGN COUNTRIES!

©1995 by King Features Syndicate, Inc. World rights reserved.

SOMEDAY I'D LIKE TO COME BACK AND SPEND MORE TIME JUST GETTING TO KNOW THE PEOPLE

LISTEN to your MOTHER

Helga tells it like it is

LISTEN to your MOTHER
Helga tells it like it is

KEEP AN OPEN MIND—YOUR MOTHER-IN-LAW IS NOT YOUR WORST ENEMY

ATTILA THE HUN IS— SHE COMES IN SECOND

(SIGH) AFTER THE DAY I'VE HAD, IT'LL BE NICE TO RELAX AND LEAVE MY TROUBLES BEHIND ME!

WHAT A NICE SURPRISE, MOTHER! HOW LONG CAN YOU STAY?

JUST A MONTH

MOTHER, IS EVERYTHING ALL RIGHT IN YOUR GUEST BEDROOM?

YES, BUT I LIKE TO SLEEP ON *TWO* PILLOWS!

I REALIZE I SAID I WANTED MY CREW TO BE ABLE TO LAUGH AND HAVE A SENSE OF HUMOR WHEN THE GOING GETS TOUGH...

HOWEVER...

TELL ME THE TRUTH, HELGA

YOUR FAMILY REUNION IS HERE THIS YEAR, ISN'T IT?

I HATE MONDAYS

THIS IS SATURDAY

I LIKE TO PLAN AHEAD